Poultry House Construction

by

Michael Roberts

Edited by Sara Roadnight

Photographs and illustrations
by Michael Roberts

Published by The Domestic Fowl Research
ISBN 0 947870 21 0

Conditions of Sale

Contents

Foreword

I have always been interested in the design of poultry houses. I have architecture in my genes, as both my uncle Hugh Roberts from Bath and my great uncle Llewellyn Roberts, who worked closely with Luytens, were outstanding architects of their time. It must be said that I am not a trained carpenter, although I took a keen interest in carpentry from the age of six, learning many techniques from our farm carpenter Bernard Bryan from Bidford on Avon. I hope you will enjoy making these houses and other items which have been on my drawing board for some three years now.

I must add that all the dimensions are in feet and inches but there is a metric conversion at the back of the book. Nearly all the timber I have used is metric, for instance 2″ × 1″ is 4.5cm × 2cm but I have put 2″ × 1″ N. (n stands for NOMINAL). So beware if you are using 2″ × 1″ ACTUAL. I am afraid metric means nothing to me!

Michael D.L. Roberts
1997

This is a typical back garden hen house knocked up with anything that came to hand, no design or planning. What a disaster, not only for the birds but for their management too!

Housing Criteria

There are many designs and types of housing available today, but few are made with the birds in mind, or daily/weekly management. Most poultry housing manufacturers don't keep hens or geese, but come into the hen house market via garden sheds and stables.

External Design - **Construction**

Most small poultry houses are made of wood, although I have seen some in Asbestos sheeting and Aluminium cladding. The wood used comes in different mediums, tongue and groove, feather-edge, ship-lap and external plyboard. External plyboard and good quality sheathing board, are the best products for making small poultry houses, providing the plyboard is kept off the ground. I have seen houses made of external ply which are 40 years old. The other key factor is that plyboard is easy to clean, and does not harbour mite, unlike T & G and ship-lap, but this is an individual preference.

Access to your poultry house is very important. You must be able to clean it, spray it, and observe all round it without having to stand on your head, or kneel down on the wet ground. Access is best through a wide door or a sliding roof.

External Design is also important. The house should look good and grace the surroundings. There is nothing worse than a poultry house which is badly designed and badly made.

All the houses I have included in this book are sectional. This is so that they can be taken to pieces periodically for cleaning, and if you move house they can be flat packed to take with you.

Internal Design

Most people don't realise that there are criteria for the internal layout of a hen house. Sizes will depend on the breed of bird that you are going to keep. There is a big difference between Brahmas and Sebrights, Cornish and Leghorns. Access to the house will be via a pop hole, and this may or not require a ramp or stepping stone. Once inside there should be enough light, via glass panels or ventilation holes, for the birds to be able to find their way about i.e. where the nest box is and how high the perches are. The floor should be solid if possible, slatted works for growers. Wire mesh floors for older birds will cause breast bone lesions. Solid floors are easier to clean as long as there is plenty of litter; this also provides a softer landing for birds coming down from the perches. (One cause of Bumble-Foot can be birds landing badly). Slatted floors become very messy and caked with manure and require soaking or power washing to clean them. Allow approximately 1.2 to 2 sq feet per bird, depending on the breed.

Nest boxes

The nest box must be in the darkest area of the house. Try not to have it facing the pop hole or window or adjacent to it. The nest box needs to be slightly raised above the level of the floor to give the bird an impression of safety. This is an original jungle fowl instinct to lay above the water line or areas which flood, and hence to build the nest a little higher.

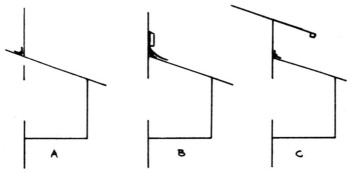

Three types of outside nest boxes. Keeping the nest box dry is essential. A: The roof of the nest box extends inside the house and is hinged inside. B: The roof of the nest box is hinged on the outside, but is covered by a waterproof membrane. C: There is an overhang of another roof which protects the roof of the nest box.

The nest box needs to be lower than the perch, so that the birds will go to the highest point in the house to roost. If the nest boxes are higher than the perches then the birds will roost or sit in the nest boxes and foul them.

The nest box should be large enough for the hens to stand up in and turn round. It also needs to be deep enough - about four inches of litter. The size will vary between 7″ × 7″ for a Sebright, to 14″ × 14″ for a Brahma. It should also be large enough for a cockerel to get into, because very often he will call the hen into the nest box with crooning noises. The hen must feel secure in there and persuaded that she is hiding her eggs, hence the darkness.

Hens need to be able to make a scrape, i.e. a concave depression in the litter, by scratching around and ruffling their feathers before laying. This is something denied to them in battery cages.

4

I have never liked separate, rather than communal nest boxes: so often I have seen eggs piled up in one nest box, because the birds prefer it to all the others. Very few eggs will get broken or starred in a communal nest box if there is sufficient litter - that is about 4" depth of shavings. Access to nest boxes is all important, not only for regular cleaning but also for the collection and observation of eggs.

The ratio of nest box space should be 3:1 or 4:1, i.e. for every three birds there should be one nest box space. Egg eating can start as a result of the nest box being too light. To counteract this put up a black plastic curtain with a staple gun to give the darkness and privacy that the hen requires. If the nest box is designed properly, this should not be a problem. (I will deal with roll-away nest boxes in another publication).

Mobility

If you are making a fold unit or house to move around there are one or two points to consider. I know some people who have built a hen house like a battle ship, and have found it too heavy to move. On the other hand, if you build an ark too long and too light, it will surely bend and break in the middle. Normally a compromise is reached with the use of wheels. I haven't any wheels on the housing in this book, but I wish to discuss these at a later time.

Perches

The standard size for perches is 2" × 2", chamfered on the top two edges. Most people think a bird stands all night, but in fact it sits on its breast on the perch, with its feet steadying it, hence if you have narrow perches these can cause an indentation in the breast bone of young birds. Perch space can vary from 5" for small bantams, like Dutch and Sebrights, up to 9" or 10" for the large breeds like Buff Orpingtons. 7" is a good average for most breeds.

Perch height is important. The lighter the breed, for instance a Leghorn or Fayomi, the higher the perch, maybe 2-3 feet high, depending on the size of the house, but down to 8" high for Cornish Game. Distance between perches can vary from 12" centres to 22" centres, again depending on the breed; with Marans for example 16" centres are about correct. Perching is all important - a bird that cannot perch well, will not lay well.

Droppings Boards

Droppings boards to collect the night manure are essential. They should be about 4" - 6" under the perches and this will ensure that the birds don't stand about in the droppings during the day, particularly if the weather is poor outside.

Ventilation

Ventilation is important, but must not cause drafts. It is quite difficult to arrange ventilation which is suitable for cold snowy winter nights or hot stuffy summer nights. The important thing is to build in flexibility. The three most common designs are drawn below.

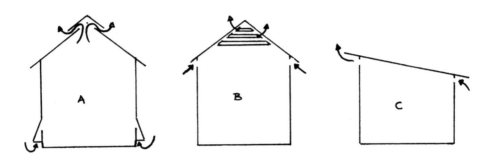

Ventilation in small houses can be made: A: with side vents and ridge ventilation, B: under-eave ventilation and apex slits, C: ventilation from the lower eaves through to the higher end.

Ventilation can be increased by having sliding shutters or doors, with a weld mesh screen behind. Some of these doors are windows as well to let light in the house, and slide vertically or horizontally. It's essential to be able to vary the amount of ventilation according to the weather conditions.

Pop holes can vary in size depending on the breed using the house. The norm is 8" wide by 10" - 12" high. The most important factor is the door closing the pop hole. It must stay up when open, and down or closed when shut. Many's the time I have seen birds locked out of their houses because the cockerel has caught his back on the bottom of the pop hole door. This has disturbed the locking mechanism, usually a hook and eye, and allowed the door to slam down behind him, so positive security mechanisms are a must to ensure that the pop hole remains open when necessary and closed against predators when necessary.

If the house is raised off the ground, you may have to put a ramp up to the pop hole or use bricks as steps. Automated pop holes can be made, but unfortunately they can't count the birds in at **night fall**, and very often hens get left outside.

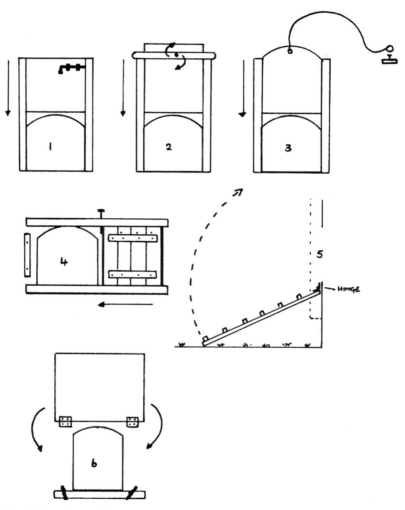

Pop Holes: 1. The door slides up and down and is fastened by a sliding bolt. 2. Here the door is held up by a rotating wooden bar. Slide the door up, rotate the bar into the vertical and lower the door. 3. Some people attach a cord to the top of the door, pull the door up, and fasten the cord, normally with a metal ring over a nail. 4. Sliding door but this needs a fastener. It can be done with a bolt, or nail dropped through the top rail. 5. Where the pop hole is raised off the ground, a ramp can be incorporated as a door. 6. A simple drop-down hinged door, with two turn buttons.

Weather Proofing

This will depend on the area you live in, the main problems being snow, high annual rainfall, gales and sun. Some of these problems can be solved by location, perhaps moving the house from a summer to a winter position. I have found Onduline bitumised roofing sheets to be very satisfactory, as they insulate the house, keeping it cool in the summer and warm in the winter. Obviously these sheets will let in driven snow, but that can be rectified with plyboard or sponge rubber cut outs. Roofing felt must never be used because it harbours red mite.

The best water repellent is Cuprinol. This is a water based wood preservative. It drys quickly, is non-toxic and comes in a range of colours. Creosote is suitable only if the house can be left to dry for several weeks. In the old days it was used as a cure-all and was splashed about the house like a disinfectant to clean up red mite or scaley leg. Anyone who has accidentally got a drop in their eye or a cut finger will know the pain it produces. But having said that, I have seen hen houses 60 and 70 years old that were regularly painted with creosote.

Hinges and Door Catches

Hinges are best used vertically rather than horizontally. In either case, they should be lubricated with oil every six months to stop them from seizing up. I try to avoid using hinges if possible.

For door catches on access doors it is best to have not only turn buttons, but also some other form of door catch. There is a wide range of metal catches on the market enabling you to shut your birds up safely, but you must make sure that the poultry house door does not work its way open on a windy night. You must always be on your guard against the ever present threat of foxes.

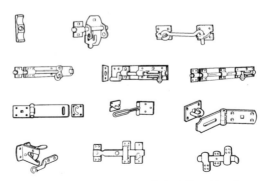

Various door catches made by Eliza Tinsley.

Tools Required

This depends on how sophisticated your workshop is, and whether you have electricity to enable you to use power tools.

Hammer, hand drill and various bits, pencil, measuring tape, set square, padsaw, sander, rip saw, tenon saw plane, staple gun, glue. *If you have electricity:* Electric drill, electric jig saw, electric planer.

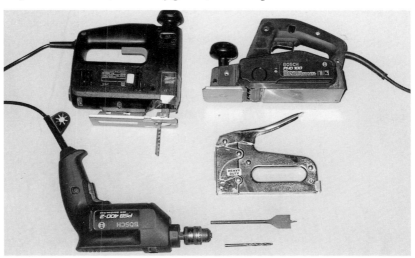

As I have pointed out elsewhere in this book I am not a carpenter, but I enjoy trying to be one. The three golden rules for making these houses are as follows:

a. Measure correctly and always double check

b. Always double set square the places where you are going to saw the wood, not only horizontally, but vertically as well. When the ends of the timber are badly cut, they stand out like "saw" thumbs!!

c. Always pre-drill to stop the wood from splitting. Split ends are not only weak but invite wood decay and look awful. (That's your carpentry lesson for the day!)

Timber Treatment

Creosote/Oil based preservatives - These forms of treatment are good if you don't have to put the birds back in their house the same day. Allow several days for the house to dry thoroughly, depending on the weather, otherwise the birds can be come discoloured by the preservative, particularly if they are white. A strong smell can also build up in the house and this can taint the eggs and make them taste of creosote.

Water based preservatives, Cuprinol, Sadoline - These preservatives are the best. They are safe to use, with a good range of colours and they dry very quickly.

Tanalith - The wood is pressure treated and is best used on fencing timbers. The preservative is arsenic based, and the timber needs to dry out thoroughly before being used, otherwise it warps badly. Tanalith seems to be more successful on certain soft woods than others.

Water/Oil dips - Many of these so called preservative dips, which you often see on garden sheds, are little more than colouring agents. It all depends on how concentrated the mixture is. It is claimed that they can do all sorts of things but after a few months exposed to the elements, they soon weather and discolour. It is best to slap on a coat of Cuprinol as soon as you can.

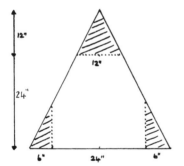

Some facts about a 6ft × 3ft × 3ft Ark

Total Cubic Capacity:	648 sq in × 72 ins long = 46656 cu ins/1728 = 27 cu ft
Less 6 cu ft. wasted area	= 21 cu ft. usable area

The same amount of timber as in the Ark above.
But the capacity is: 792 sq in × 72 ins long
= 57024 cu ins/1728
= 33 cu ft total usable area.

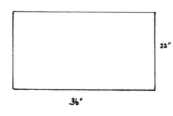

When I studied the old books on housing and catalogues of that time, there were very few Arks described. However in the 1930s people began to run cattle and sheep together with poultry, and the Ark was designed with a pointed roof to stop sheep and lambs from jumping on top of it. In reality however, it is a wasteful design as you can see from the diagrams. For almost the same amount of timber as the rectangular design, the Ark loses a 1/3 of its capacity.

11

Duck Nest Boxes

Ducks need somewhere to lay their eggs away from the prying eyes of crows and magpies. Both these houses have baffles inside, so if the crow/magpie looks in it cannot see the nest. Both nest boxes are easy to check, as they have hinged rooves. The lower nest box can be used for Mandarin or Carolina ducks, providing there is a ladder or log of wood for the duck to clamber up. In this case the nest box should be placed about 3ft off the ground.

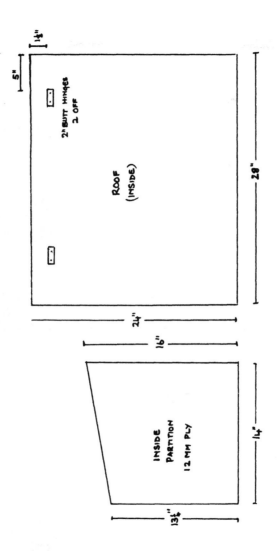

ROOF
(INSIDE)

2" BUTT HINGES
2 OFF

1¼"

5"

28"

24"

INSIDE
PARTITION
12 MM PLY

9"

14"

13¼"

Duck Nest Boxes

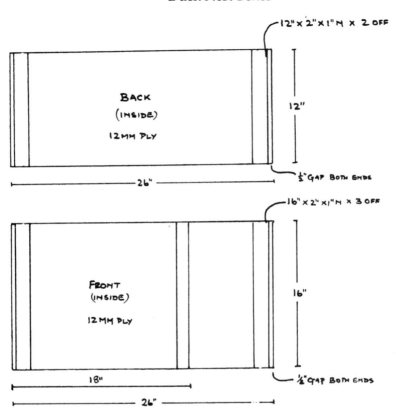

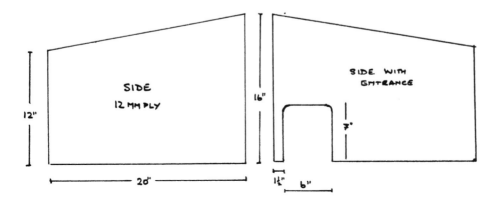

Duck Nest Boxes

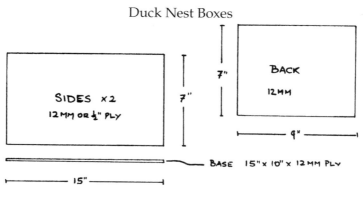

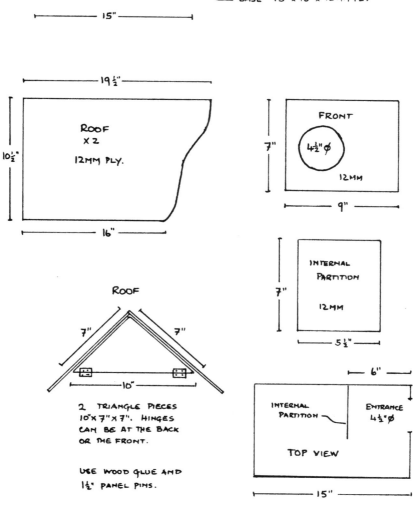

SIDES x2
12MM OR ½" PLY

7"

15"

BACK
12MM

7"

9"

BASE   15" x 10" x 12MM PLY

ROOF
X 2
12MM PLY.

19½"

10½"

16"

FRONT

4½" ⌀

12MM

7"

9"

INTERNAL PARTITION
12MM

7"

5½"

ROOF

7"   7"

10"

2 TRIANGLE PIECES
10" X 7" X 7". HINGES
CAN BE AT THE BACK
OR THE FRONT.

USE WOOD GLUE AND
1½" PANEL PINS.

INTERNAL PARTITION

ENTRANCE
4½" ⌀

6"

TOP VIEW

15"

Internal Nest Boxes

These nest boxes are useful where birds are housed in a shed or stable. The steeply sloping roof prevents the birds from roosting on it.

Internal Nest Boxes

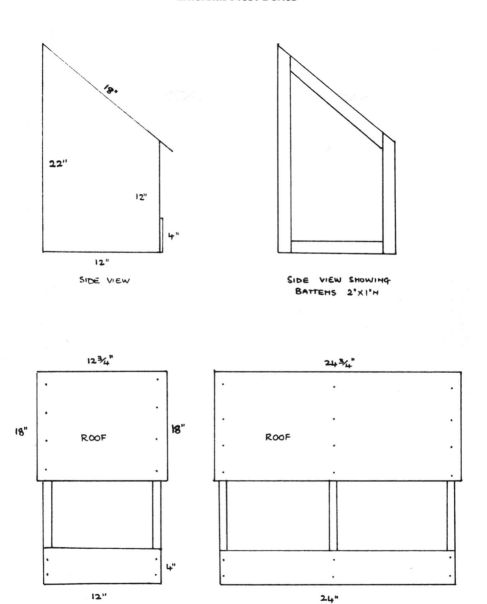

SIDE VIEW

SIDE VIEW SHOWING
BATTENS 2"X1"H

ROOF

ROOF

FRONT

Broody/Bantam/Rabbit Coop

This was designed as a multi-purpose coop, with two different centre sections, one for a broody and chicks and the other for a trio of bantams or a pet rabbit. Access is very easy, the roof slides forward, revealing a perch and droppings board, with a nest box underneath. Both these items are removable for cleaning or converting into a broody coop.

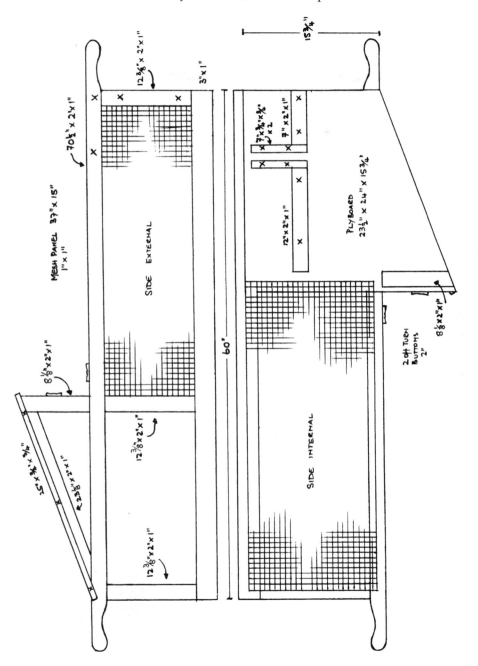

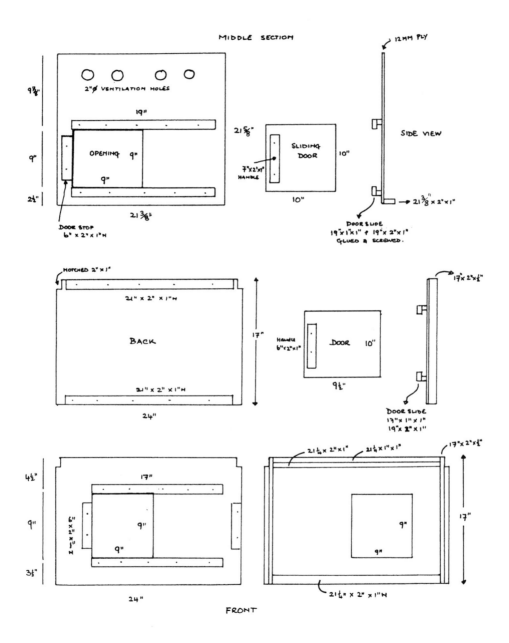

MIDDLE SECTION

2"Ø VENTILATION HOLES

9⅜"

19"

9"

OPENING   9"

9"

2¼"

21⅜"

DOOR STOP
6" x 2" x 1" H

21⅝"

SLIDING
DOOR

10"

7"x2"x1"
HANDLE

10"

12MM PLY

SIDE VIEW

→ 21⅜" x 2" x 1"

DOOR SLIDE
19"x1"x1" & 19"x 2" x 1"
GLUED & SCREWED.

NOTCHED 2" x 1"

24" x 2" x 1" H

BACK

24" x 2" x 1" H

24"

17"

HANDLE
6"x2"x1"

DOOR   10"

9½"

17"x 2"x½"

DOOR SLIDE
17"x 1" x 1"
19"x 2" x 1"

4½"

17"

9"

6" x 2" x 1"

9"

9"

3½"

24"

FRONT

21¼" x 2"x1"   21¼"x 1" x 1"

17"x 2"x½"

9"

9"

17"

21¼" x 2" x 1" H

Broody/Bantam/Rabbit Coop

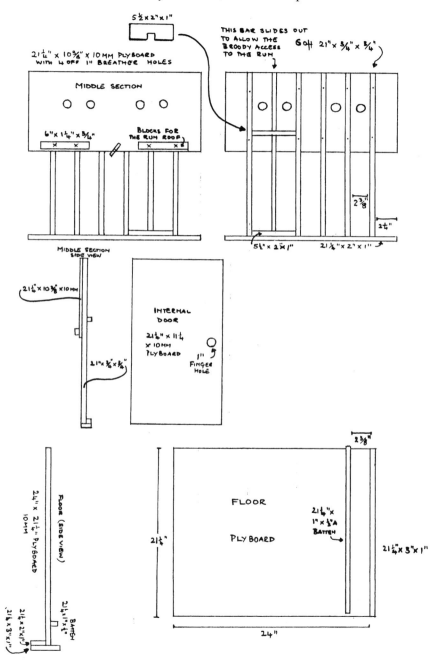

$5\frac{1}{2} \times 2" \times 1"$

THIS BAR SLIDES OUT
TO ALLOW THE
BROODY ACCESS
TO THE RUN

6 off $21" \times \frac{3}{4}" \times \frac{3}{4}"$

$21\frac{1}{4}" \times 10\frac{3}{8}" \times 10MM$ PLYBOARD
WITH 4 OFF 1" BREATHER HOLES

MIDDLE SECTION

$6" \times 1\frac{1}{4}" \times \frac{3}{4}"$

BLOCKS FOR
THE RUN ROOF

$2\frac{3}{8}"$

$2\frac{1}{4}"$

MIDDLE SECTION
SIDE VIEW

$5\frac{1}{2}" \times 2" \times 1"$

$21\frac{1}{4}" \times 2" \times 1"$

$21\frac{1}{4}" \times 10\frac{3}{8}" \times 10MM$

INTERNAL
DOOR

$21\frac{1}{4}" \times 11\frac{1}{4}"$
$\times 10MM$
PLYBOARD

1"
FINGER
HOLE

$21" \times \frac{3}{4}" \times \frac{3}{4}"$

$2\frac{3}{8}"$

$24" \times 21\frac{1}{4}"$ PLYBOARD
10MM

FLOOR (SIDE VIEW)

FLOOR

PLYBOARD

$21\frac{1}{4}" \times$
$1" \times \frac{1}{2}"A$
BATTEN

$21\frac{1}{4}" \times 3" \times 1"$

$21\frac{1}{2}"$

$24"$

BATTEN
$21\frac{1}{4}" \times \frac{1}{2}"$

$21\frac{1}{4} \times 2" \times 1"$

$21\frac{1}{4} \times 3" \times 1"$

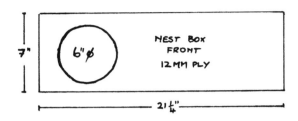

7"

6" ∅

NEST BOX
FRONT
12 MM PLY

21 1/4"

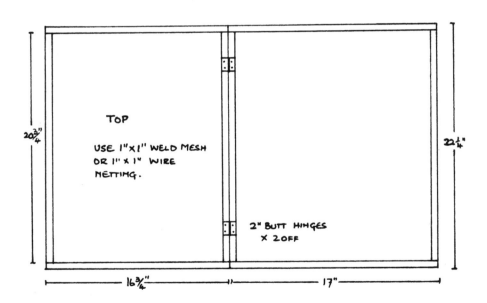

TOP

USE 1"x1" WELD MESH
OR 1" x 1" WIRE
NETTING.

2" BUTT HINGES
X 2 OFF

20 3/4"

22 1/4"

16 3/4"

1"

17"

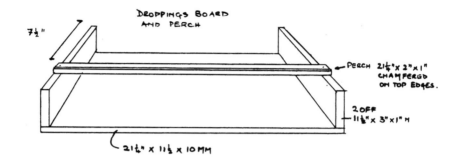

DROPPINGS BOARD
AND PERCH

7½"

PERCH 21½" x 2" x 1"
CHAMFERGD
ON TOP EDGES.

2 OFF
11½" x 3" x 1" H

21½" x 11½ x 10 MM

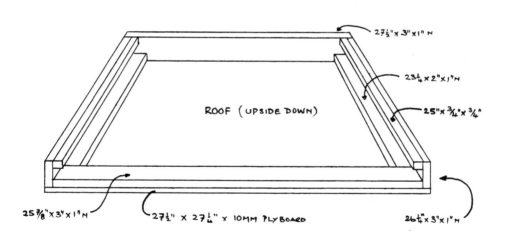

27½" x 3" x 1" H

23¼ x 2" x 1" H

25" x ¾" x ¾"

ROOF (UPSIDE DOWN)

25⅜" x 3" x 1" H

27½" x 27¼" x 10 MM PLYBOARD

26¼" x 3" x 1" H

Broody Boxes

If you are using broodies to hatch out your eggs, then these boxes are invaluable. They need to be placed away from your other hens, in the shade of a tree and on slightly raised ground. The full details on using these boxes are covered in *Incubation at Home*. I remember, as a boy, helping the game keeper hatch pheasant and partridge eggs, using two long banks of these boxes. I got to know each broody and her character - some were real old battle axes, while others were really meek and even-tempered.

Broody Boxes

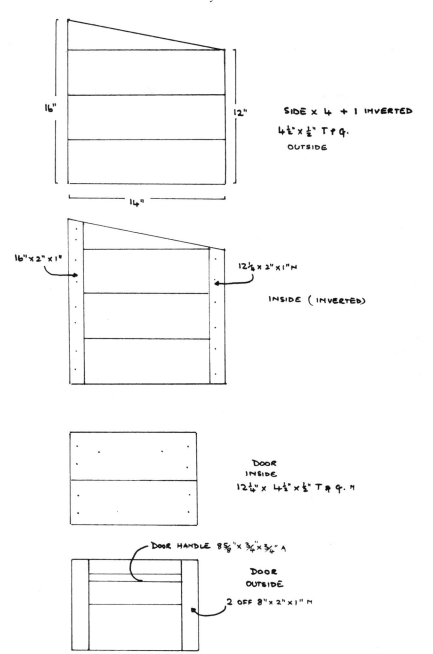

16"

12"

14"

SIDE x 4 + 1 INVERTED
4½" x ½" T & G.
OUTSIDE

16" x 2" x 1"

12⅛ x 2" x 1" N

INSIDE (INVERTED)

DOOR
INSIDE
12¼" x 4½" x ½" T & G. M

DOOR HANDLE 8⅝" x ¾" x ¾" A

DOOR
OUTSIDE

2 OFF 8" x 2" x 1" M

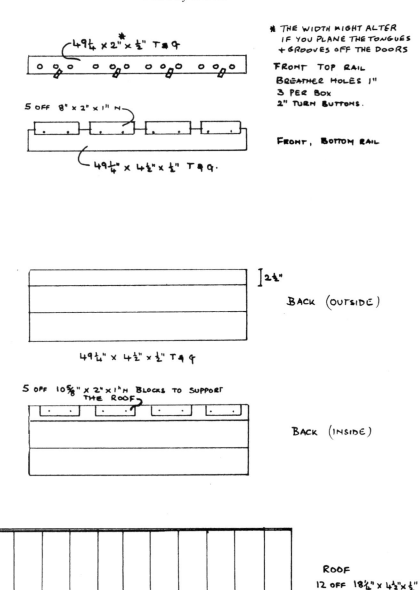

$49\frac{1}{4}'' \times 2'' \times \frac{1}{2}''$ T & G

5 OFF $8'' \times 2'' \times 1''$ H

$49\frac{1}{4}'' \times 4\frac{1}{2}'' \times \frac{1}{2}''$ T & G.

* THE WIDTH MIGHT ALTER
IF YOU PLANE THE TONGUES
+ GROOVES OFF THE DOORS

FRONT TOP RAIL
BREATHER HOLES 1''
3 PER BOX
2'' TURN BUTTONS.

FRONT, BOTTOM RAIL

$2\frac{1}{4}''$

BACK (OUTSIDE)

$49\frac{1}{4}'' \times 4\frac{1}{2}'' \times \frac{1}{2}''$ T & G

5 OFF $10\frac{5}{8}'' \times 2'' \times 1''$ H BLOCKS TO SUPPORT
THE ROOF.

BACK (INSIDE)

ROOF
12 OFF $18\frac{1}{4}'' \times 4\frac{1}{2}'' \times \frac{1}{2}''$
T & G.

Anti-Broody Coop or Sin Bin

This contraption is designed to make a broody hen feel as uncomfortable as possible. It has a weld mesh floor so that the broody has a constant draft of air around her nether regions. She should be fed on plain wheat and fresh water. The house is *not* fox proof and needs to be put in a fox proof area. Some of my earliest memories are of my grandmother's Marans in her anti-broody coop which I still use today, probably more than 60 years later.

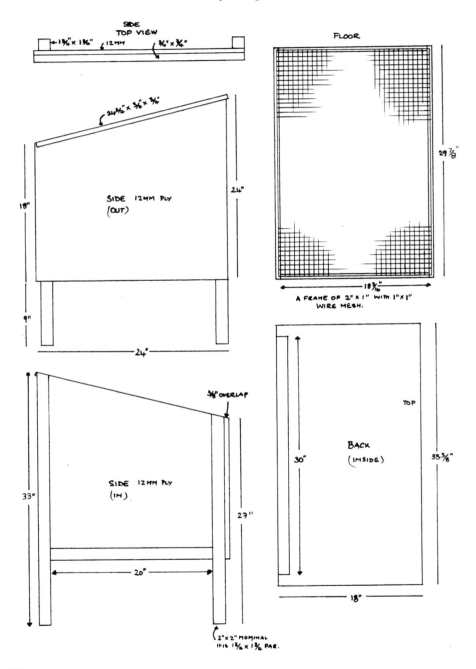

SIDE TOP VIEW

1¾" x 1½"   12MM   ¾" x ¾"

24½" x ¾" x ¾"

SIDE 12MM PLY
(OUT)

18"   24"

9"

24"

FLOOR

29⅞"

18¾"

A FRAME OF 2" X 1" WITH 1" X 1"
WIRE MESH.

⅜" OVERLAP

SIDE 12MM PLY
(IN)

33"   27"

20"

2" X 2" NOMINAL
1F IS 1¾" x 1¾" PAR.

TOP

BACK
(INSIDE)

30"   33⅜"

18"

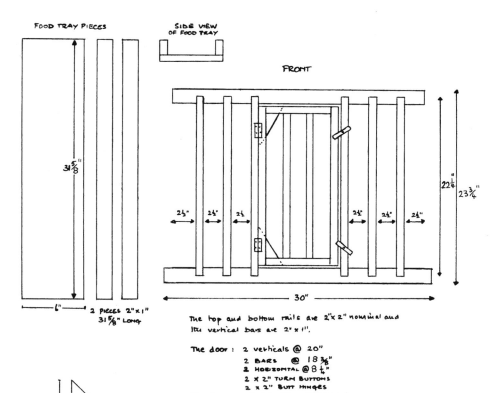

FOOD TRAY PIECES

SIDE VIEW
OF FOOD TRAY

FRONT

31⅝"

6"

2 PIECES 2"x1"
31⅝" LONG

2½" 2½" 2½"   2½" 2½" 2½"

30"

22¼" 23¾"

The top and bottom rails are 2"x 2" nominal and
the vertical bars are 2" x 1".

The door : 2 verticals @ 20"
           2 BARS   @ 18⅜"
           2 HORIZONTAL @ 8½"
           2 X 2" TURN BUTTONS
           2 x 2" BUTT HINGES

The door is nailed together. There are two
6"x 6" GUSSETS ON THE BACK OF THE DOOR
TO STRENGTHEN THE DOOR. (6MM PLY)

6" 12MM

6"

4 GUSSETS TO SUPPORT
WIRE MESH FLOOR.
NOTCHED IN CORNER
2"x 2" N

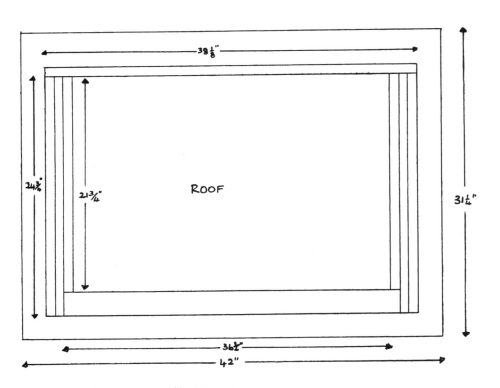

ROOF

38⅛"

24⅞"

21¾"

31¼"

36½"

42"

ROOF : 42" × 31¼" × 12MM

1 × 38⅛ × 3 × 1
2 × 24¾" × 3" × 1"
2 × 21¾ × 2" × 1"
2 × 21¾ × ¾" × ¾"
1 × 36½ × 3" × 1"

Trap Nest Box

I have studied these in detail as there are several types and techniques that have been produced over the years by various manufacturers all claiming all sorts of advantages. I was asked to manufacture some for the Rare Breeds Survival Trust, and this is the design I choose.

There are two important points about trap nest boxes:

1. The mechanism must not put the hen off or frighten her but must be positive.

2. There must be a lobby incorporated in the design, so that once the bird has laid her egg, she can move off the nest. If this does not happen, 9 times out of 10 the egg will be cracked by the hen impatient to get out of the nest box.

Using this system, the wire trigger which holds up the sliding door can be used first without the door, so the hens get used to pushing past the trigger. When the trigger is set, the door closes gently on to the bird's tail. It must be said that you should do your recording as soon as possible when using trap nest boxes for your laying birds, as it is cruel to leave them cooped up inside for hours, but it is certainly a very revealing and rewarding exercise.

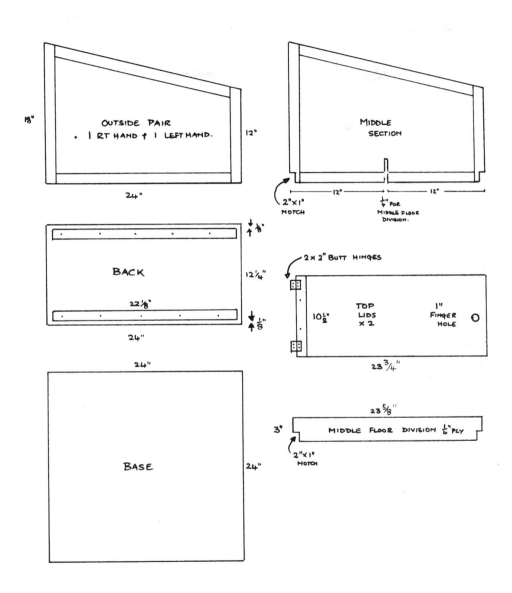

OUTSIDE PAIR
• 1 RT HAND & 1 LEFT HAND.

18"

12"

24"

MIDDLE
SECTION

2"×1"
NOTCH

12"

¼" FOR
MIDDLE FLOOR
DIVISION.

12"

BACK

⅛"

12¼"

22⅛"

⅛"

24"

24"

2 × 2" BUTT HINGES

TOP
LIDS
× 2

10½"

1"
FINGER
HOLE

O

23¾"

BASE

24"

24"

23⅝"

3"

MIDDLE FLOOR DIVISION ¼" PLY

2"×1"
NOTCH

33

Trap Nest Box

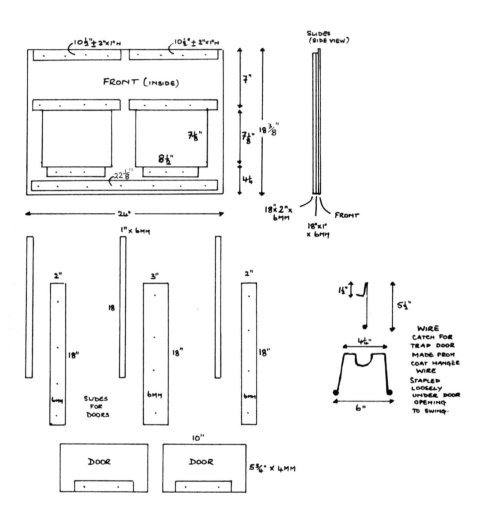

34

Show Box

With the increasing intrusion of common market dictates, the days of arriving at your local poultry show with your birds in cardboard boxes are probably numbered. I have always thought this design of show box to be the most practical, and the slide-out divisions make cleaning that much easier. Birds do not require any food or water while travelling and in cool weather they will be alright for up to 8 hours. Food and water in the show box only make a mess of the birds and the box, and as already mentioned, birds don't eat while travelling anyway.

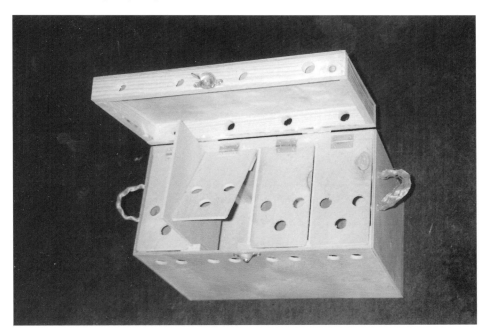

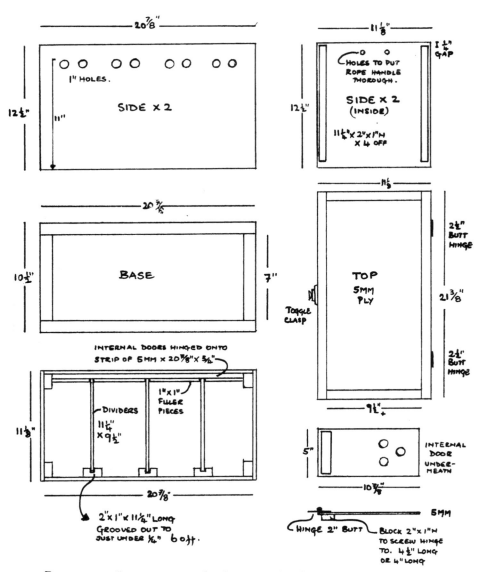

BUILD THE BASE FIRST. THEN BUILD UP THE SIDES,
GLUEING AND SCREWING THE CORNER BATTENS 2"X1" X 11¼" LONG.
CUT AND GROOVE THE DIVIDER HOLDERS AND GLUE AND SCREW
INTO PLACE.

Bantam House

This is a cheap and easy house to make and I have used this type for years. It is simple to clean out as the sliding roof gives complete access to the inside of the house, which is divided into three - a nest box, a perching area and a feeding/day area. The verandah on the front allows the birds to go out without getting their feet wet or muddy.

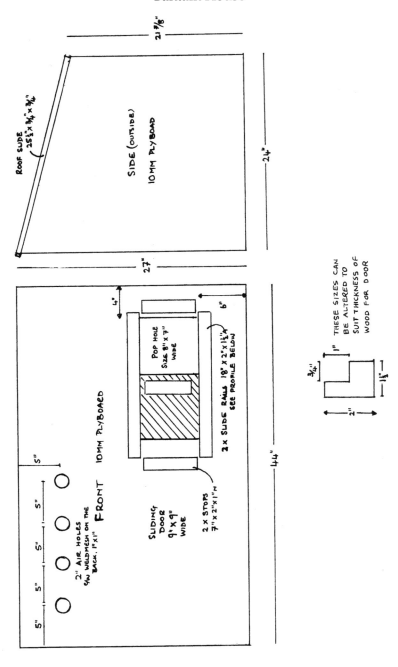

ROOF SLIDE
25½" x 3¾" x ¾"

SIDE (OUTSIDE)
10MM PLYBOARD

21 ⅞"

24"

27"

4"

6"

POP HOLE
SIZE 8" x 7" WIDE

2 x SLIDE RAILS 18" x 2" x 1½" N
SEE PROFILE BELOW

2 x STOPS
7" x 2" x 1" N

SLIDING
DOOR
9" x 9"
WIDE

2" AIR HOLES
¼" WELDMESH ON THE
BACK, 1" x 1"

FRONT   10MM PLYBOARD

5"   5"   5"   5"   5"   5"   5"

44"

THESE SIZES CAN
BE ALTERED TO
SUIT THICKNESS OF
WOOD FOR DOOR

¾"

1"

1½"

2"

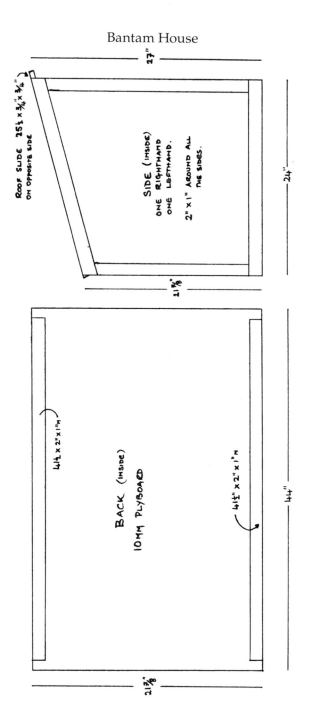

ROOF SLIDE $25\frac{1}{4}$" × $\frac{3}{4}$" × $\frac{3}{4}$"
ON OPPOSITE SIDE

SIDE (INSIDE)

ONE RIGHTHAND
ONE LEFTHAND.

2" × 1" AROUND ALL
THE SIDES.

23"

24"

$21\frac{7}{8}$"

$44\frac{1}{2}$" × 2" × 1"N

$41\frac{1}{2}$" × 2" × 1"N

BACK (INSIDE)

10MM PLYBOARD

44"

$21\frac{7}{8}$"

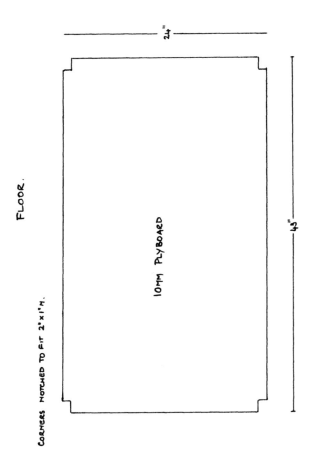

FLOOR.

10MM PLYBOARD

CORNERS NOTCHED TO FIT 2" x 1" H.

2'4"

4'3"

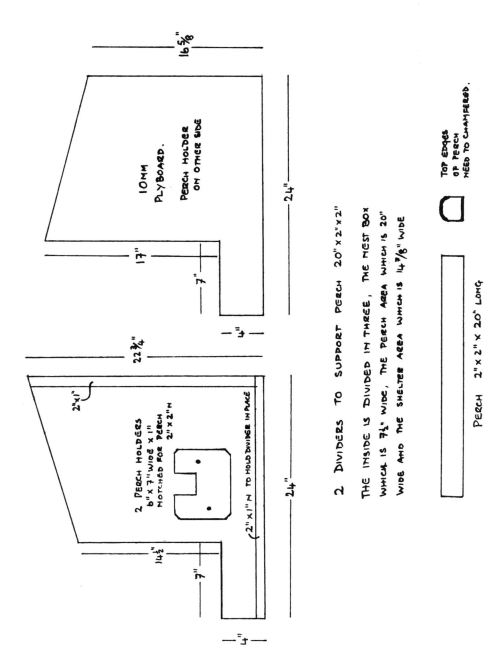

16 5/8"

10MM
PLYBOARD.

PERCH HOLDER
ON OTHER SIDE

24"

17"

7"

1/4"

22 3/4"

2"x1"

2 PERCH HOLDERS
6" x 7" WIDE x 1"
NOTCHED FOR PERCH
2" x 2"

(2" x 1" N TO HOLD DIVIDER IN PLACE

24"

14 1/2"

7"

1/4"

2 DIVIDERS TO SUPPORT PERCH 20" x 2" x 2"

THE INSIDE IS DIVIDED IN THREE, THE NEST BOX
WHICH IS 7 1/2" WIDE, THE PERCH AREA WHICH IS 20"
WIDE AND THE SHELTER AREA WHICH IS 14 7/8" WIDE

TOP EDGES
OF PERCH
NEED TO CHAMFERED.

PERCH 2" x 2" x 20" LONG

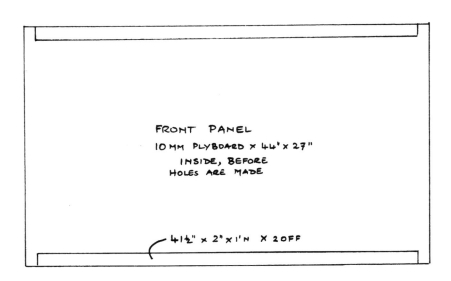

FRONT PANEL

10 MM PLYBOARD x 44' x 27"

INSIDE, BEFORE
HOLES ARE MADE

41½" x 2" x 1'N X 2OFF

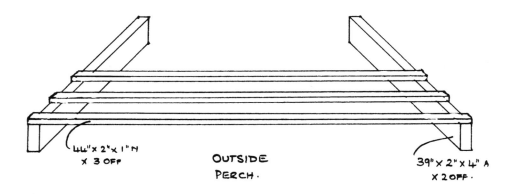

44"x 2'x 1"N
X 3 OFF

OUTSIDE
PERCH.

39"x 2"x 4" A
X 2OFF.

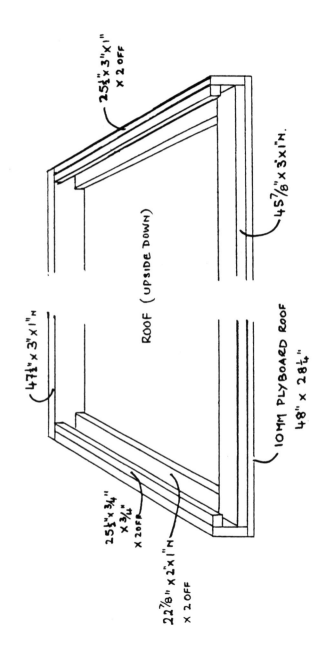

25¼" × 3" × 1"
X 2 OFF

45⁷/₈" × 3" × 1" N.

ROOF (UPSIDE DOWN)

47¼" × 3" × 1" N

10MM PLYBOARD ROOF
48" × 28¼"

25⅛" × 3¼"
× ³/₄"
X 2FF

22⁷/₈" × 2" × 1" N
X 2 OFF

8ft Run

This is a very simple and easy run to construct. It is light-weight but the advantage of this design is access. It is easy to catch birds inside this run, and feeding and watering are very straightforward.

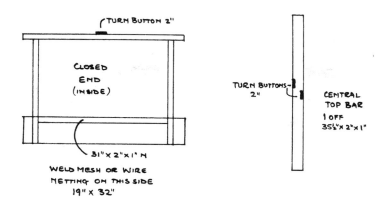

TURN BUTTON 2"

CLOSED
END
(INSIDE)

31" X 2" X 1" N

WELD MESH OR WIRE
NETTING ON THIS SIDE
19" X 32"

TURN BUTTONS –
2"

CENTRAL
TOP BAR
1 OFF
35½" X 2" X 1"

HINGED TOPS X 2

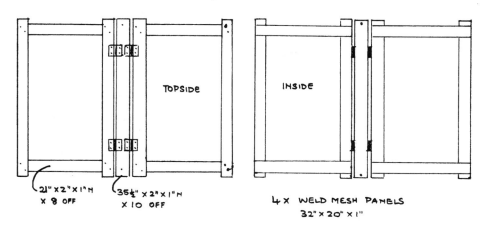

TOPSIDE

INSIDE

21" X 2" X 1" N
X 8 OFF

35½" X 2" X 1" N
X 10 OFF

4 X WELD MESH PANELS
32" X 20" X 1"

45

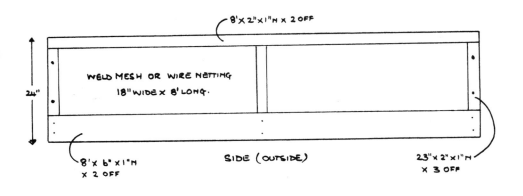

8' X 2" X 1" H X 2 OFF

WELD MESH OR WIRE NETTING
18" WIDE X 8' LONG.

24"

SIDE (OUTSIDE)

8' X 6" X 1" H
X 2 OFF

23" X 2" X 1" H
X 3 OFF

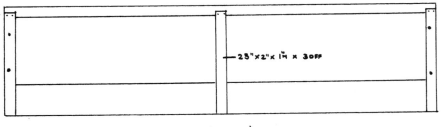

23" X 2" X 1" H X 3 OFF

SIDE (INSIDE)

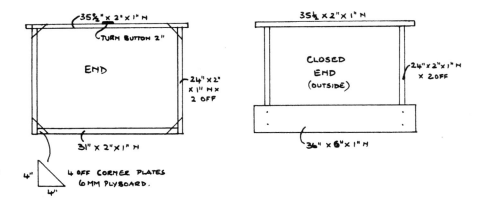

35½" X 2" X 1" H

TURN BUTTON 2"

END

24" X 2"
X 1" H X
2 OFF

31" X 2" X 1" H

4"

4"

4 OFF CORNER PLATES
6MM PLYBOARD.

35½" X 2" X 1" H

CLOSED
END
(OUTSIDE)

24" X 2" X 1" H
X 2 OFF

36" X 6" X 1" H

6ft Ark

The Ark is made with hinged sides, and the three triangular sections are screwed into place. Ideal for a few growers or a rabbit, it has a solid wood floor and no perch. The door is slightly different in the drawing compared to the photograph. Note that the door-side of the Ark is one inch shorter than the other sides; care must be taken to ensure that the cladding is nailed on to the correct side, otherwise the air will be blue when you come to assemble it in the garden!

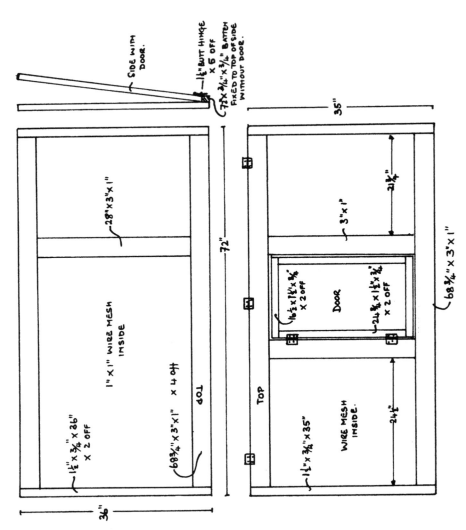

THE SIDE PANELS OF THE
ARK ARE HINGED AT THE
TOP

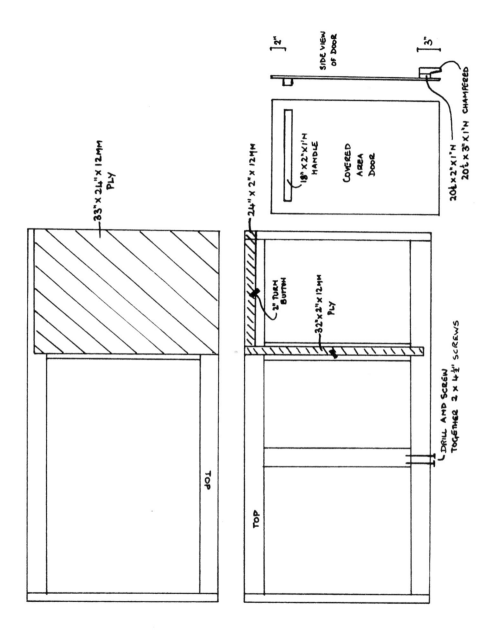

]2"

SIDE VIEW OF DOOR

]3"

20½ x 2" x 1" CHAMFERED

18" x 2" x 1" HANDLE

COVERED AREA DOOR

83" x 24" x 12MM PLY

24" x 2" x 12MM

2" TURN BUTTON

32" x 2" x 12MM PLY

DRILL AND SCREW TOGETHER 2 x 4½" SCREWS

TOP

TOP

49

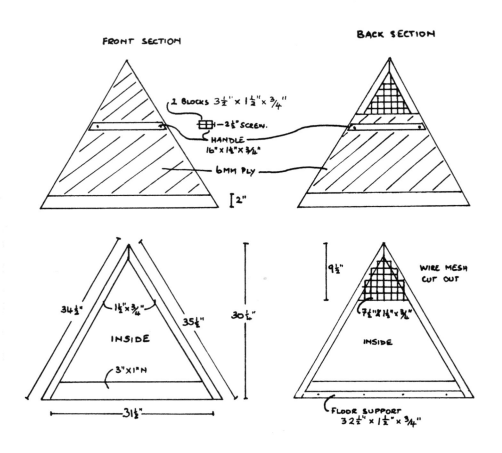

FRONT SECTION

BACK SECTION

2 BLOCKS $3\frac{1}{2}'' \times 1\frac{1}{2}'' \times \frac{3}{4}''$

4 – $2\frac{1}{2}''$ SCREW.

HANDLE
$16'' \times 1\frac{1}{4}'' \times \frac{3}{4}''$

6MM PLY

$[2''$

$34\frac{1}{2}''$ $1\frac{1}{2}'' \times \frac{3}{4}''$

$35\frac{1}{4}''$

$30\frac{1}{4}''$

INSIDE

$3'' \times 1'' \text{N}$

$31\frac{1}{2}''$

$9\frac{1}{2}''$

WIRE MESH
CUT OUT

$7\frac{1}{4}'' \times 1\frac{1}{4}'' \times \frac{3}{4}''$

INSIDE

FLOOR SUPPORT
$32\frac{1}{4}'' \times 1\frac{1}{2}'' \times \frac{3}{4}''$

BEWARE : WHEN CONSTRUCTING THESE TRIANGULAR SECTIONS, REMEMBER THAT ONE SIDE IS LONGER THAN THE OTHER. ENSURE YOU PUT THE CLADDING ON THE CORRECT SIDE.

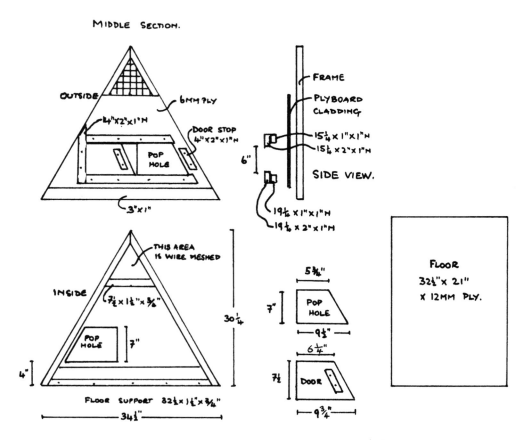

MIDDLE SECTION.

OUTSIDE

6MM PLY

4"x2"x1"H

DOOR STOP
4"X2"X1"H

POP HOLE

3"x1"

FRAME

PLYBOARD CLADDING

$15\frac{1}{4}$ X 1" X 1" H

$15\frac{1}{8}$ X 2" X 1" H

6"

SIDE VIEW.

$19\frac{1}{6}$ X 1" X 1" H

$19\frac{1}{6}$ X 2" X 1" H

THIS AREA IS WIRE MESHED

INSIDE

$7\frac{1}{2}$ X $1\frac{1}{2}$" X $\frac{3}{8}$"

POP HOLE

7"

$30\frac{1}{4}$

4"

FLOOR SUPPORT $32\frac{1}{2}$ X $1\frac{1}{2}$" X $\frac{3}{4}$"

$34\frac{1}{2}$"

$5\frac{3}{4}$"

POP HOLE

7"

$9\frac{1}{2}$"

$6\frac{1}{4}$"

DOOR

$7\frac{1}{2}$

$9\frac{3}{4}$"

FLOOR
$32\frac{1}{2}$" X 21"
X 12MM PLY.

51

8ft Ark

This is about as large as you can get with an Ark, before it bends in the middle, or becomes too heavy to move, without resorting to wheels or a gorilla! Weld mesh (1″ × 1″) is essential for this house to maintain its rigidity and strength; also weld mesh is badger/fox proof. The plyboard cladding should be on the outside and not the inside as per photograph.

8ft Ark

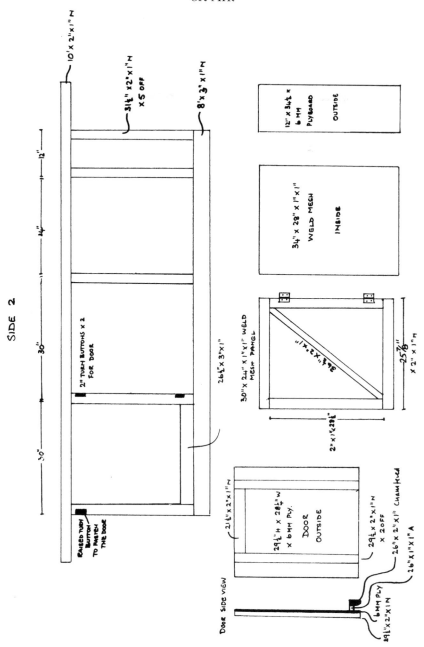

SIDE 2

10' x 2" x 1" H

31¼" x 2" x 1" H
x 5 OFF

8' x 3" x 1" H

12"

4"

30"

8"

30"

2" TURN BUTTONS x 2
FOR DOOR

26¼" x 3" x 1"

RAISED TURN
BUTTON
TO MATCH
THE DOOR

12" x 34½" x
6 MM
PLYBOARD

OUTSIDE

34" x 28" x 1" x 1"
WELD MESH

INSIDE

30" x 24" x 1" x 1" WELD
MESH PANEL

34¼" x 2" x 1"

25⅞"
x 2" x 1" H

2" x 1" x 29½"

DOOR SIDE VIEW

21¼" x 2" x 1"

29¼" H x 28½" W
x 6 MM PLY.

DOOR
OUTSIDE

29¼ x 2" x 1" H
x 2 OFF

26" x 2" x 1" CHAMFERED

26" x 1" x 1" A

6 MM PLY
2" x 1 IN

29¼" x 2" x 1 IN

53

SIDE 1

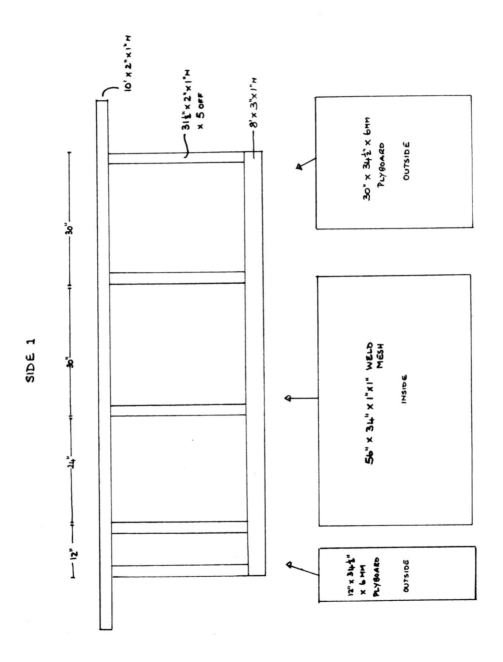

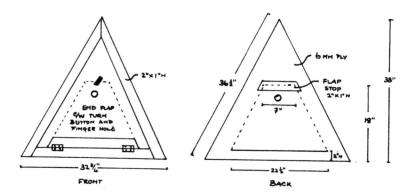

END SECTION SHOWING ACCESS FLAP.

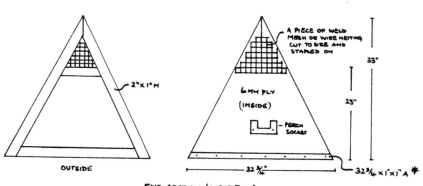

END SECTION (NEST BOX)

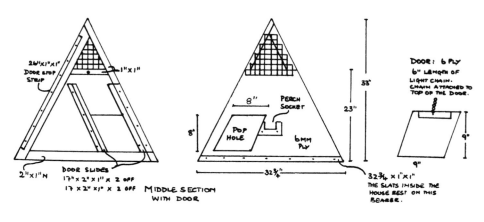

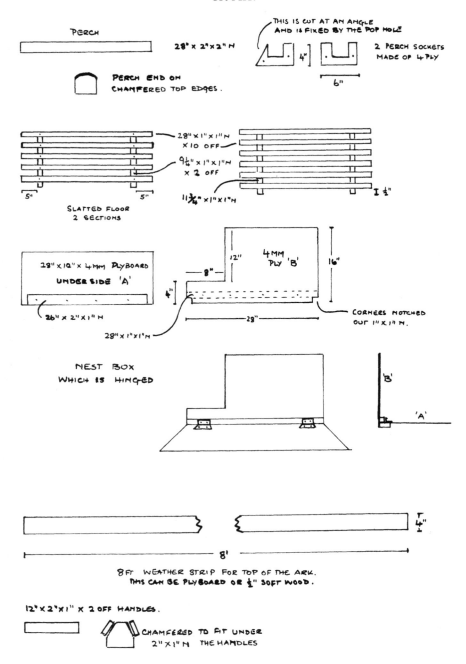

PERCH

28" x 2" x 2" H

THIS IS CUT AT AN ANGLE
AND IS FIXED BY THE POP HOLE

4"

6"

2 PERCH SOCKETS
MADE OF 4 PLY

PERCH END OH
CHAMFERED TOP EDGES.

28" x 1" x 1" H
X 10 OFF

9¼" x 1" x 1" H
x 2 OFF

11¾" x 1" x 1" H

I ½"

5"   5"

SLATTED FLOOR
2 SECTIONS

28" x 10" x 4 MM PLYBOARD
UNDER SIDE 'A'

26" x 2" x 1" H

28" x 1" x 1" H

12"

8"

4"

4 MM
PLY 'B'

16"

29"

CORNERS NOTCHED
OUT 1" x 1" H.

NEST BOX
WHICH IS HINGED

'B'

'A'

8'

4"

8 FT WEATHER STRIP FOR TOP OF THE ARK.
THIS CAN BE PLYBOARD OR ¼" SOFT WOOD.

12" x 2" x 1" X 2 OFF HANDLES.

2" x 1" H

CHAMFERED TO FIT UNDER
THE HANDLES

Free Range Feeder

This is a feeder/shelter I designed some years ago in order to feed young growers and adults without the wild birds taking the food, or the food getting wet. The feeder should be positioned with the perspex sheet facing the wind. The sliding roof panels allow access to the two plastic food hoppers (15 kilos). If you notice that starlings or other wild birds are finding the food, just fit a plastic curtain with vertical slits to the two entrance areas. This feeder can accommodate 200 growers or 50 adult hens.

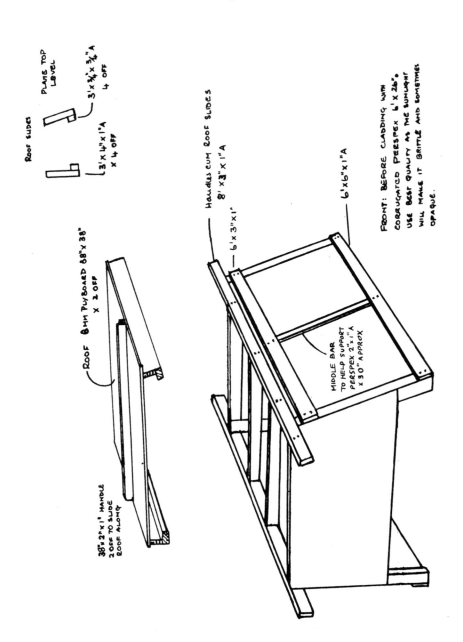

ROOF SLIDES

PLANE TOP
LEVEL

3' x ¾" x ¾" A
4 OFF

[3' x 4" x 1" A
x 4 OFF

HANDLES CUM ROOF SLIDES

8' x 3" x 1" A

6' x 3" x 1"

6' x 6" x 1" A

ROOF 8MM PLYBOARD 68" x 38"
x 2 OFF

MIDDLE BAR
TO HELP SUPPORT
PERSPEX 2" x 1" A
x 30" APPROX

FRONT: BEFORE CLADDING WITH
CORRUGATED PERSPEX 6' x 26'.
USE BEST QUALITY AS THE SUNLIGHT
WILL MAKE IT BRITTLE AND SOMETIMES
OPAQUE.

38" x 2" x 1" HANDLE
2 OFF TO SLIDE
ROOF ALONG

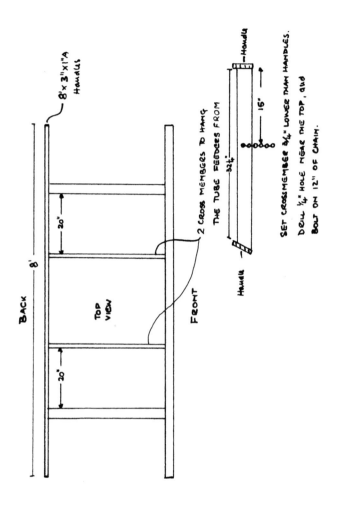

8' x 3" x 1" A
Handles

8'

BACK

20"

TOP
VIEW

20"

FRONT

2 CROSS MEMBERS TO HANG
THE TUBE FEEDERS FROM

Handle

32½"

16"

Handle

SET CROSSMEMBER ¾" LOWER THAN HANDLES.
DRILL ¼" HOLE NEAR THE TOP, AND
BOLT ON 12" OF CHAIN.

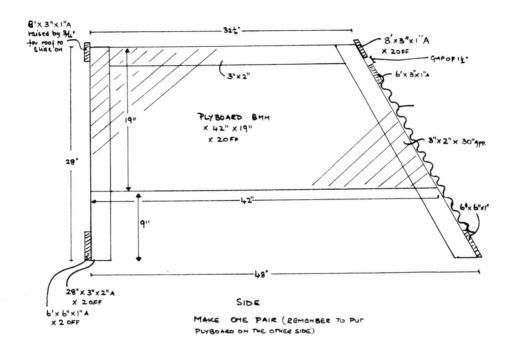

8' x 3" x 1" A
raised by 3/4"
for roof to
slide on

32½'

8' x 3" x 1" A
X 2 OFF

GAP OF 1½"

6' x 3" x 1" A

3" x 2"

PLYBOARD 8MM
X 42" X 19"
X 2 OFF

19"

28"

3" x 2" x 30" 4PP.

42"

6' x 6" x 1"

9"

48"

28" X 3" X 2" A
X 2 OFF

6' x 6" x 1" A
X 2 OFF

SIDE

MAKE ONE PAIR (REMEMBER TO PUT
PLYBOARD ON THE OTHER SIDE)

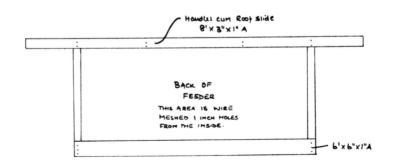

Handle cum Roof slide
8' x 3" x 1" A

BACK OF
FEEDER
THIS AREA IS WIRE
MESHED 1 INCH HOLES
FROM THE INSIDE.

6' x 6" x 1" A

The Eight-Hen House

This is a labour-saving house which is easy to construct. There is a large sliding roof which allows complete access to the house for egg collection and cleaning. The droppings board and perch are combined and are fitted over the nest box. They slide for access to the nest box and there is adjustable ventilation on the front. This house will accommodate 6 Buff Orpingtons, 8 light breeds, like Leghorns or Warrens, or 10 bantams.

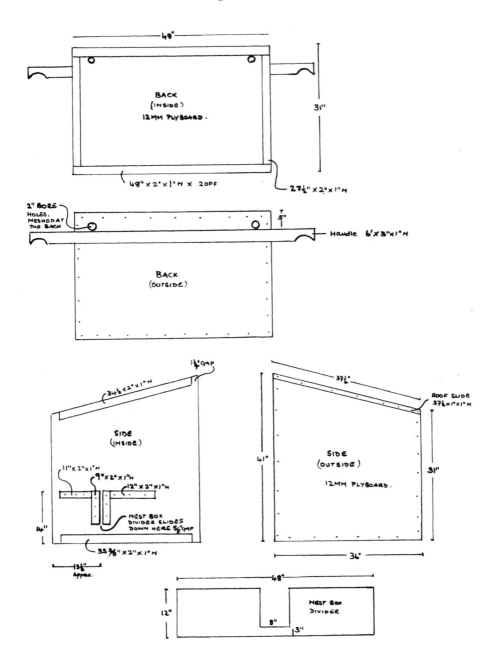

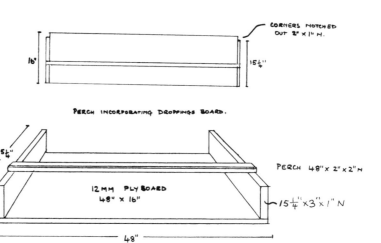

CORNERS NOTCHED OUT 2" x 1" H.

16"

15¼"

PERCH INCORPORATING DROPPINGS BOARD.

15¼"

PERCH 48" x 2" x 2" H

12 MM PLY BOARD
48" x 16"

15¼" x 3" x 1" N

48"

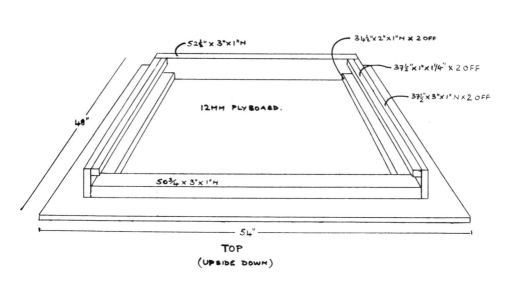

52¼" x 3" x 1" H

34¼" x 2" x 1" H x 2 OFF

37½" x 1" x 1¼" x 2 OFF

37½" x 3" x 1" N x 2 OFF

12 MM PLYBOARD.

48"

50¾ x 3" x 1" H

54"

TOP
(UPSIDE DOWN)

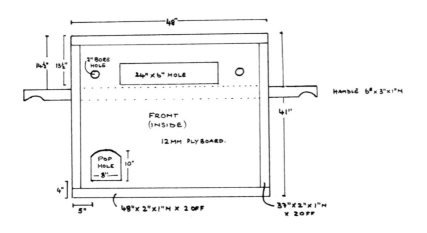

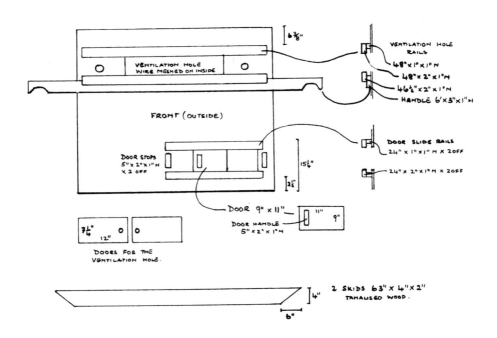

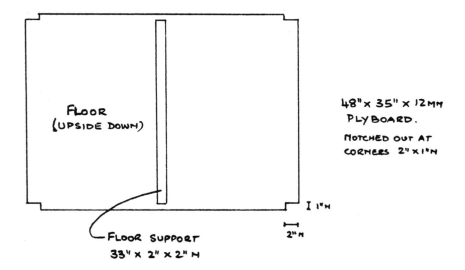

FLOOR
(UPSIDE DOWN)

FLOOR SUPPORT
33" × 2" × 2" M

48" × 35" × 12MM
PLYBOARD.
NOTCHED OUT AT
CORNERS 2" × 1"M

I 1"M

2" M

The Ten-Hen House

This is a convenient house for 10 hens, which includes an outside nest box, a droppings board, 2 perches and a large access door on the side. The lift-up roof over the perches allows for easy weekly cleaning of the droppings board. The floor should be cleaned out every 4 - 6 weeks depending on the weather. Ventilation is via two under-roof cut-outs. This house is on skids to stop rats from living underneath.

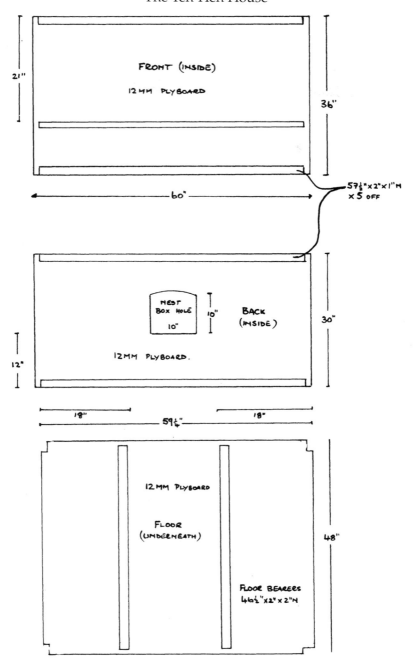

FRONT (INSIDE)

12 MM PLYBOARD

21"

36"

60"

57½"×2"×1"H
× 5 OFF

NEST
BOX HOLE

10"

10"

BACK
(INSIDE)

30"

12MM PLYBOARD.

12"

18"

59¼"

18"

12 MM PLYBOARD

FLOOR
(UNDERNEATH)

48"

FLOOR BEARERS
46½"×2"×2"H

The Ten-Hen House

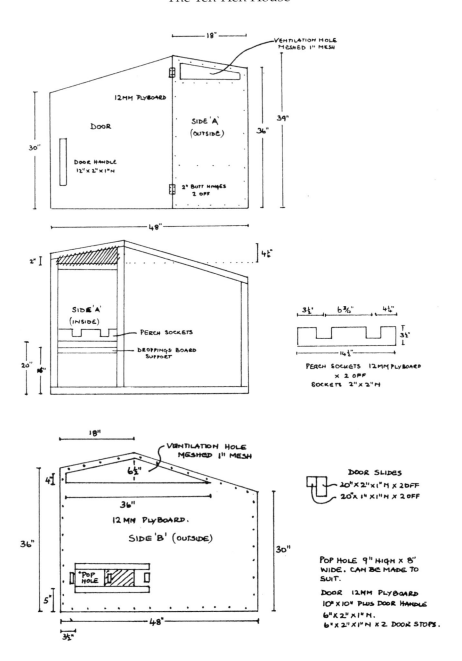

68

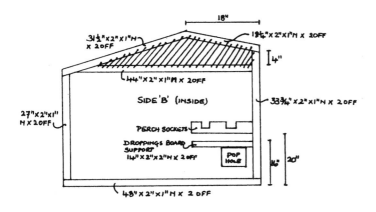

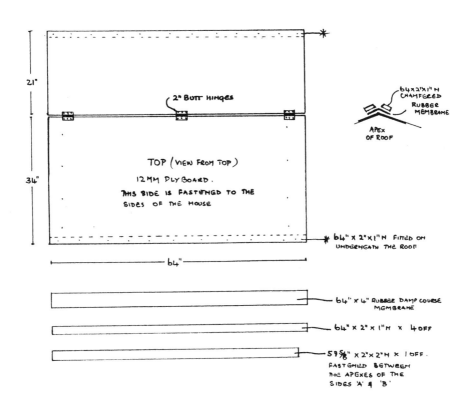

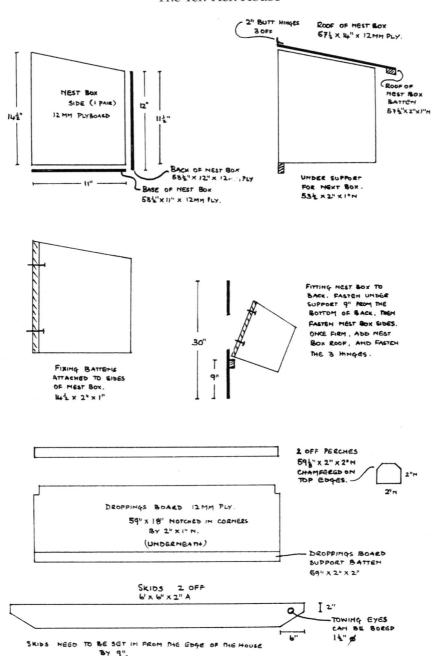

2" BUTT HINGES
3 OFF

ROOF OF NEST BOX
57½" X 14" X 12MM PLY.

NEST BOX
SIDE (1 PAIR)
12 MM PLYBOARD

14½"

12"

11½"

ROOF OF
NEST BOX
BATTEN
57½"X2"X1"N

BACK OF NEST BOX
53½" X 12" X 12MM PLY

BASE OF NEST BOX
53½"X 11" X 12MM PLY.

11"

UNDER SUPPORT
FOR NEST BOX.
53½ X 2" X 1"N

FIXING BATTENS
ATTACHED TO SIDES
OF NEST BOX.
14½ X 2" X 1"

30"

9"

FITTING NEST BOX TO
BACK. FASTEN UNDER
SUPPORT 9" FROM THE
BOTTOM OF BACK. THEN
FASTEN NEST BOX SIDES.
ONCE FIRM, ADD NEST
BOX ROOF, AND FASTEN
THE 3 HINGES.

2 OFF PERCHES
59½" X 2" X 2"N
CHAMFERED ON
TOP EDGES.

2"N

2"N

DROPPINGS BOARD 12MM PLY.
59" X 18" NOTCHED IN CORNERS
BY 2" X 1" N.
(UNDERNEATH)

DROPPINGS BOARD
SUPPORT BATTEN
59" X 2" X 2"

SKIDS 2 OFF
6' X 6" X 2" A

2"

TOWING EYES
CAN BE BORED
1½" ∅

6"

SKIDS NEED TO BE SET IN FROM THE EDGE OF THE HOUSE
BY 9".

Fold Unit

This house incorporates several good ideas, including room for your feet when moving it, a covered food and water shelf, good access from the top, enough height for large birds like Brahmas or Dorkings, retractable handles and a sliding roof over the nest box and perching area. It must be made in light plyboard, otherwise it is too heavy to lift.

Fold Unit

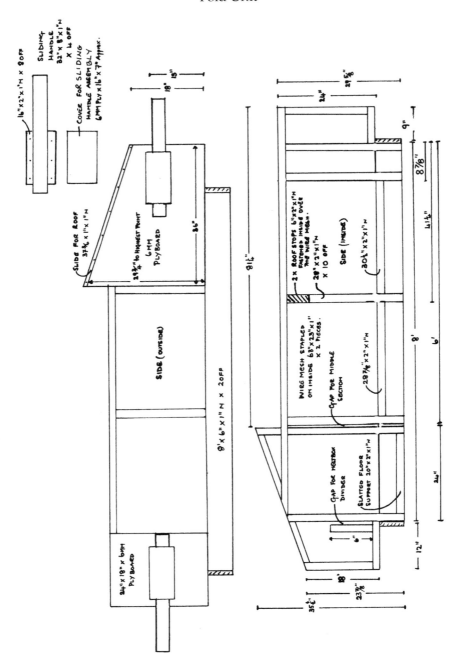

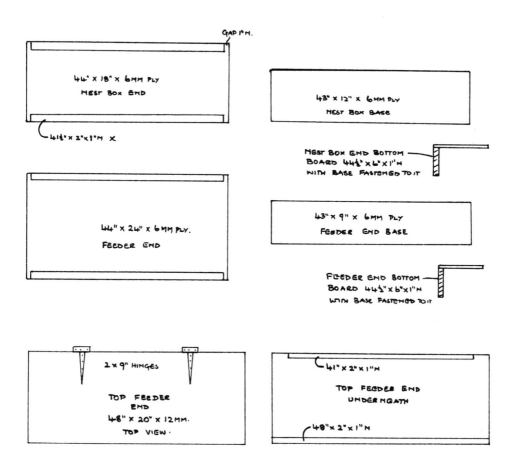

GAP 1"H.

44" X 18" X 6MM PLY
NEST BOX END

└ 41¼" X 2"X1"H X

44" X 24" X 6MM PLY.
FEEDER END

43" X 12" X 6MM PLY
NEST BOX BASE

NEST BOX END BOTTOM ─
BOARD 44½" X 6" X 1"N
WITH BASE FASTENED TO IT

43" X 9" X 6MM PLY
FEEDER END BASE

FEEDER END BOTTOM ─
BOARD 44½" X 6"X1"N
WITH BASE FASTENED TO IT

2 X 9" HINGES

TOP FEEDER
END
48" X 20" X 12MM.
TOP VIEW·

└ 41" X 2" X 1"N

TOP FEEDER END
UNDERNEATH

└ 48"X 2" X 1" N

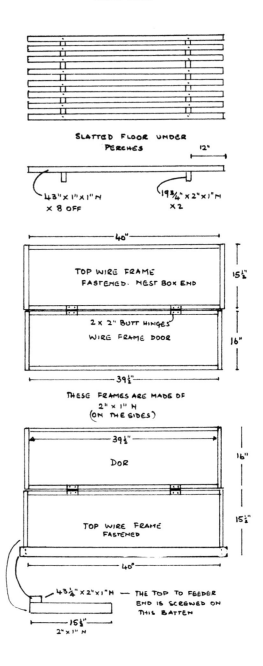

SLATTED FLOOR UNDER
PERCHES

12"

43" x 1" x 1" H
x 8 OFF

19¾" x 2" x 1" H
x2

40"

TOP WIRE FRAME
FASTENED. NEST BOX END

15½"

2 x 2" BUTT HINGES

WIRE FRAME DOOR

16"

39½"

THESE FRAMES ARE MADE OF
2" x 1" H
(ON THE SIDES)

39½"

DOR

16"

TOP WIRE FRAME
FASTENED

15½"

40"

43¼" x 2" x 1" H — THE TOP TO FEEDER
END IS SCREWED ON
THIS BATTEN

15½"
2" x 1" H

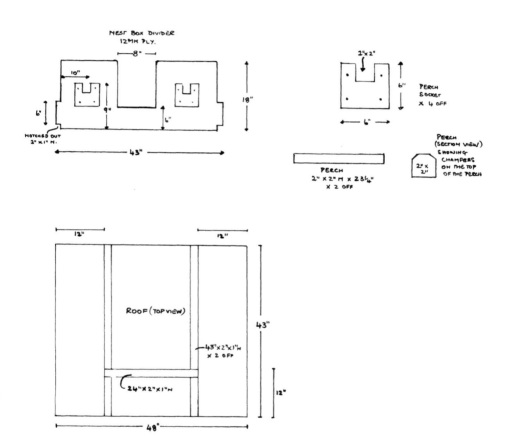

NEST BOX DIVIDER
12MM PLY.

8"

10"

9"

6"

18"

NOTCHED OUT
2" X 1" N.

43"

2" X 2"

6"

PERCH
SOCKET
X 4 OFF

6"

PERCH
2" X 2" M X 23½"
X 2 OFF

PERCH
(SECTION VIEW)
SHOWING
CHAMFERS
ON THE TOP
OF THE PERCH

2" X
2"

12"

12"

ROOF (TOP VIEW)

43"

43" X 2" X 1" H
X 2 OFF

24" X 2" X 1" H

12"

48"

Fold Unit

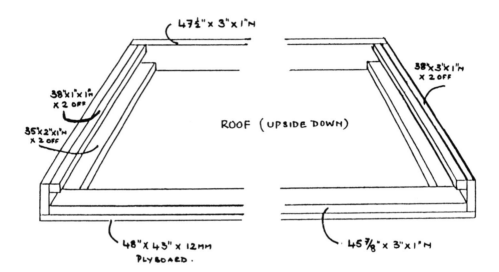

47½" x 3" x 1"N

38"x3"x1"N
x 2 OFF

38"x1"x1"N
x 2 OFF

35"x2"x1"N
x 2 OFF

ROOF (UPSIDE DOWN)

48" X 43" X 12MM
PLYBOARD.

45⅞" x 3" x 1"N

MIDDLE SECTION (INSIDE)

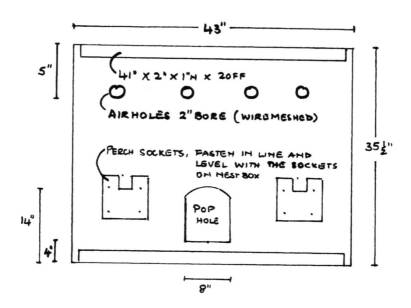

43"

5"

41" X 2" X 1"H X 2OFF

AIRHOLES 2"BORE (WIREMESHED)

PERCH SOCKETS, FASTEN IN LINE AND LEVEL WITH THE SOCKETS ON NEST BOX

35½"

POP HOLE

14"

4"

8"

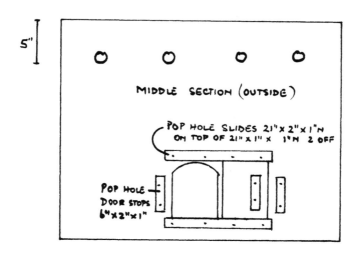

5"

MIDDLE SECTION (OUTSIDE)

POP HOLE SLIDES 21" X 2" X 1"H ON TOP OF 21" X 1" X 1"H 2 OFF

POP HOLE DOOR STOPS 6"X2"X1"

The Poultry Palace

In designing this I wanted a static house for a small garden which could be used for hens or bantams, or, with some conversion, for pigeons and doves. It is very easy to make, giving the birds maximum floor space with a nest box area and perching area above. There is access at the back to all these areas for feeding, egg collection, cleaning and inspection. A full length door on the side allows access to the front, and the roof consists of three sheets of Onduline.

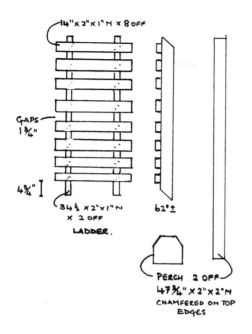

14" x 2" x 1" H x 8 OFF

GAPS 1¾"

4¾"

34½ x 2" x 1" H X 2 OFF

LADDER.

62° ±

PERCH 2 OFF
47¾" X 2" X 2" H
CHAMFERED ON TOP
EDGES

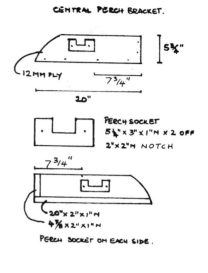

CENTRAL PERCH BRACKET.

5¾"

12 MM PLY

7¾"

20"

PERCH SOCKET
5¼" X 3" X 1" H X 2 OFF
2" X 2" H NOTCH

7¾"

20" X 2" X 1" H
4⅝ X 2" X 1" H

PERCH SOCKET ON EACH SIDE.

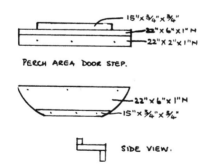

15" X ¾" X ¾"
22" X 6" X 1" H
22" X 2" X 1" H

PERCH AREA DOOR STEP.

22" X 6" X 1" H
15" X ¾" X ¾"

SIDE VIEW.

ONDULINE IS CORRUGATED BITUMEN FELT
ROOFING SHEETS FROM FRANCE.
SIZE: 79½" X 36" OR 2M X 1M. WHERE
ONDULINE IS NOT AVAILABLE, I WOULD SUGGEST
12 MM OR ½" PLYBOARD PAINTED WITH A BITUMEN
PAINT OR COATING.

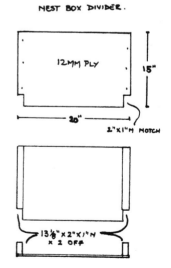

NEST BOX DIVIDER.

12 MM PLY

15"

20"

2" X 1" H NOTCH

13⅛" X 2" X 1" H
X 2 OFF

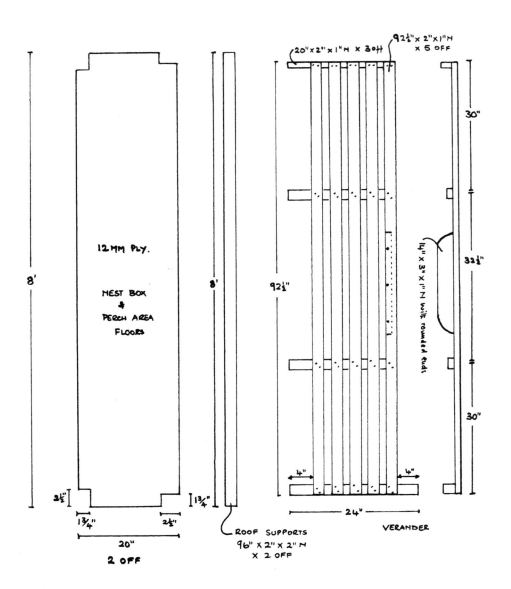

8'

12 MM PLY.

NEST BOX
&
PERCH AREA
FLOORS

2¹⁄₂"

1³⁄₄"   2¹⁄₂"

20"

2 OFF

8'

1³⁄₄"

ROOF SUPPORTS
96" X 2" X 2" M
X 2 OFF

20" X 2" X 1" M X 30ff

92¹⁄₂" X 2" X 1" M
X 5 OFF

92¹⁄₂"

1¹⁄₄" X 3" X 1" M with rounded ends

4"   4"

24"

VERANDER

30"

32¹⁄₂"

30"

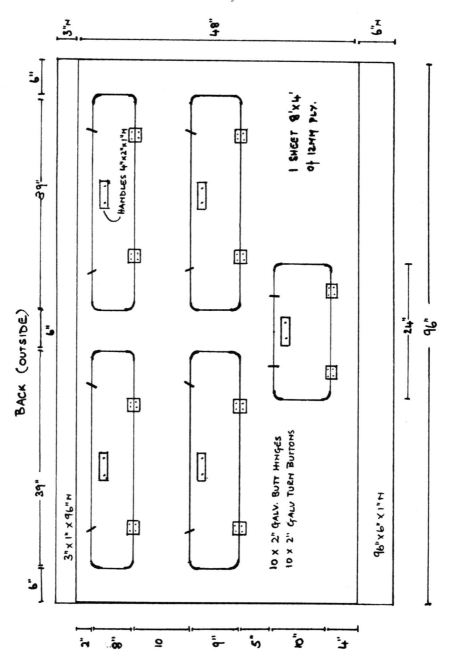

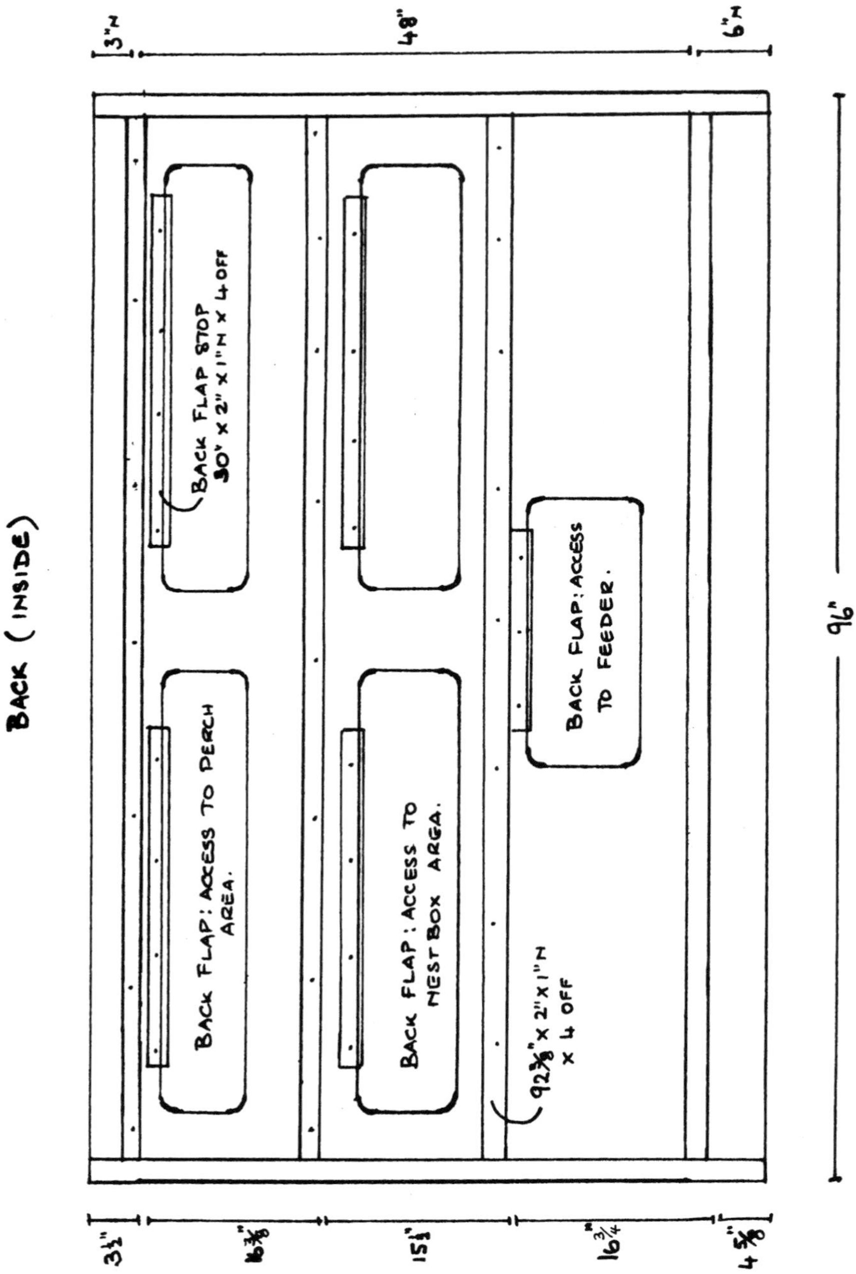

BACK (INSIDE)

3" | 48" | 6"9"

9'6"

BACK FLAP STOP
30" x 2" x 1" x 4 OFF

BACK FLAP: ACCESS TO PERCH
AREA.

BACK FLAP: ACCESS TO
NEST BOX AREA.

BACK FLAP: ACCESS
TO FEEDER.

92⅜" x 2" x 1" x 4 OFF

3½" | 16⅜" | 15¼" | 16¾" | 4⅝"

SIDE (OUTSIDE)

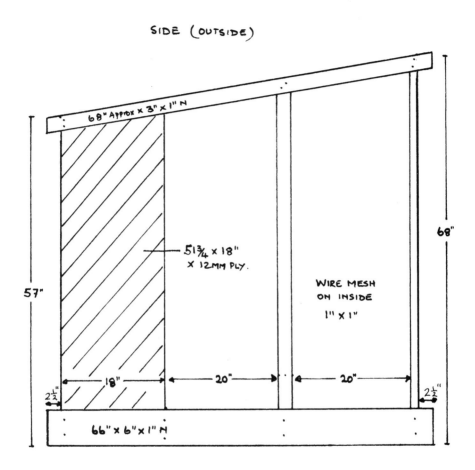

68" Approx x 3" x 1" N

68"

57"

$51\frac{3}{4}$ × 18"
× 12MM PLY.

WIRE MESH
ON INSIDE
1" × 1"

18"

20"

20"

$2\frac{1}{2}$"

$2\frac{1}{2}$"

66" x 6" x 1" N

SIDE (INSIDE)

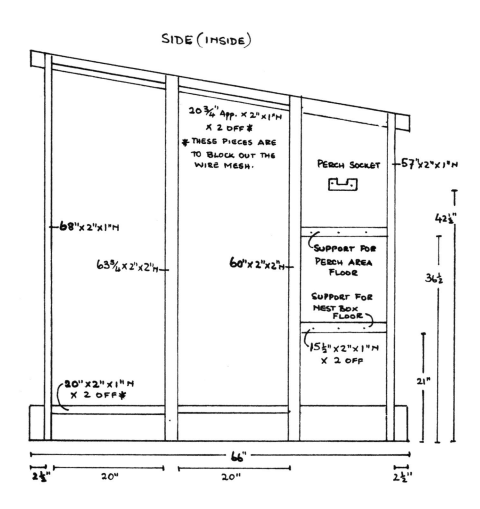

SIDE WITH DOOR (INSIDE)

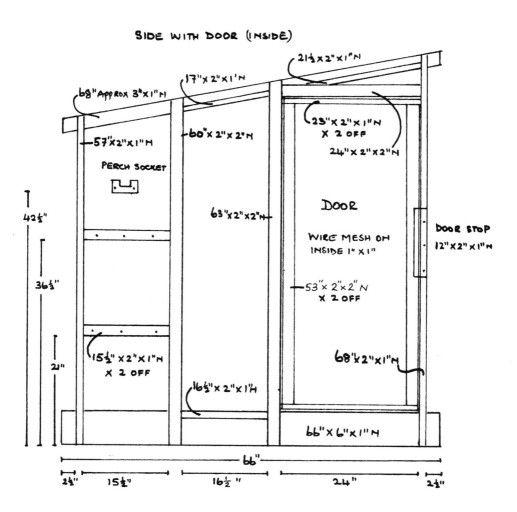

21½"x2"x1"N

17"x2"x1"N

68" APPROX 3"x1"N

23"x2"x1"N
X 2 OFF

24"x2"x2"N

57"x2"x1"N

60"x 2"x 2"N

PERCH SOCKET

63"x2"x2"N

DOOR

WIRE MESH ON
INSIDE 1"x1"

DOOR STOP
12"x2"x1"N

42½"

36½"

53"x 2"x 2" N
X 2 OFF

21"

15½"x2"x1"N
X 2 OFF

68"x2"x1"N

16½"x2"x1¼H

66"x 6"x1"N

66"

2¼"   15½"   16½ "   24"   2¼"

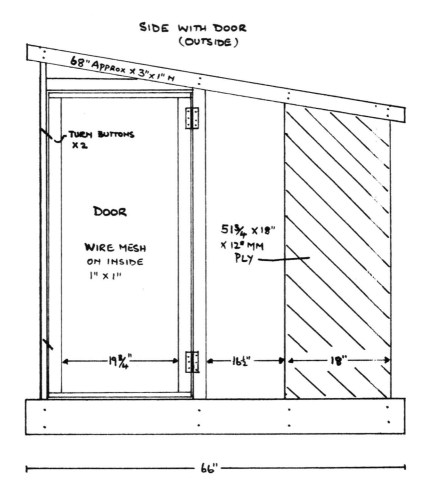

SIDE WITH DOOR
(OUTSIDE)

68" APPROX X 3"X 1" H

TURN BUTTONS
X 2

DOOR

WIRE MESH
ON INSIDE
1" X 1"

51¾ X 18"
X 12" MM
PLY

19¾"

16½"

18"

66"

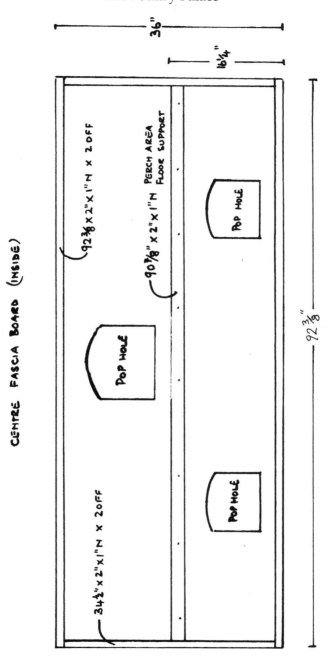

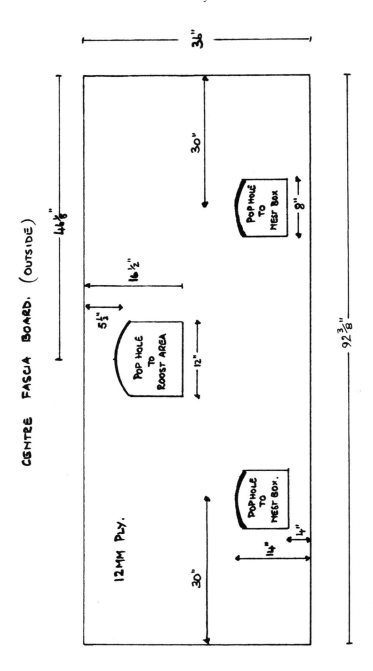

CENTRE FASCIA BOARD. (OUTSIDE)

12MM PLY.

36"

44⅛"

92⅜"

30"

30"

16½"

5½"

12"

POP HOLE TO ROOST AREA

POP HOLE TO NEST BOX

8"

POPHOLE TO NEST BOX.

14"

4"

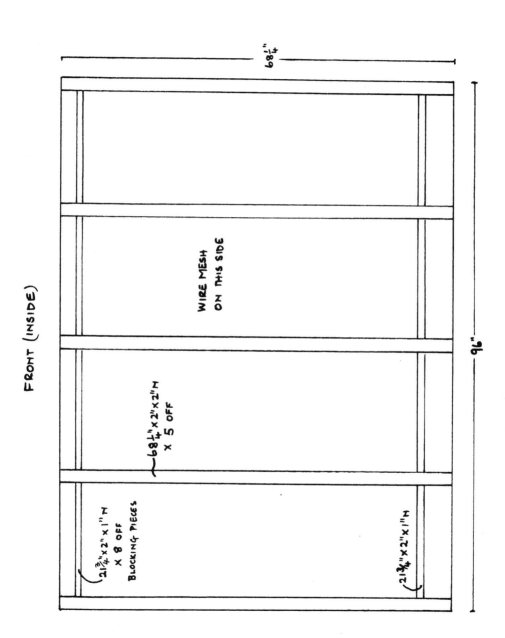

FRONT (INSIDE)

68¼"

96"

WIRE MESH
ON THIS SIDE

68¼" x 2" x 2" H
x 5 OFF

21¾" x 2" x 1" H
x 8 OFF
BLOCKING PIECES

21¾" x 2" x 1" H

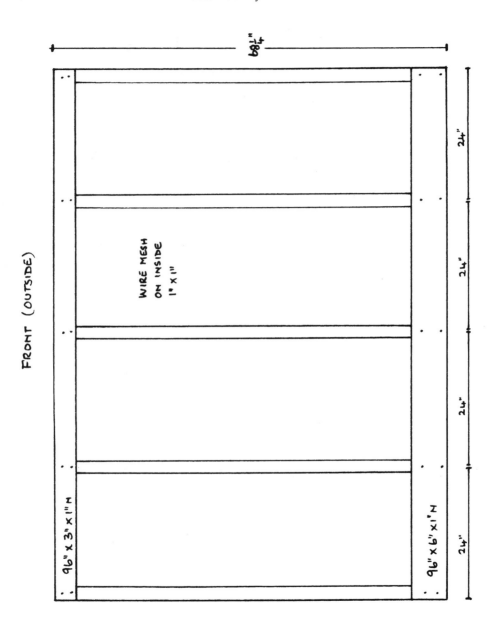

FRONT (OUTSIDE)

48¼"

24"

24"

24"

24"

WIRE MESH
ON INSIDE
1" X 1"

96" X 3" X 1" M

96" X 6" X 1" M

For the more metric minded readers, here is a conversion chart.

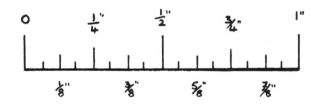

Shown larger than actual size

Inches denoted by ", i.e. 14" = 14 inches
Feet denoted by ' i.e. 6' = 6 feet
There are 12" to 1 foot (Feet plural of foot)
1" = 2.5 cm approx. 80 cms = 31½"
12" = 30.5 cms